Holy Island off Arran showing both lighthouses, (J Love)

The Island Lighthouses
of Scotland

by John A Love

'Whenever I smell salt water, I know that I am not far away from one of the works of my ancestors.'

Robert Louis Stevenson, 1880

Published in 2011 by The Islands Book Trust
www.theislandsbooktrust.com

Copyright John Love 2011

Cover image: Isle of Stroma, Caithness (J Love)

ISBN 978-1-907443-26-8

Islands Book Trust
Ravenspoint
Kershader
Lochs
Isle of Lewis
Scotland
HS2 9QA
Tel 01851 880737

Shore Print and Design Ltd.
Office 4 Clinton's Yard, Rigs Road, Stornoway
Isle of Lewis HS1 2RF.

Ardnamurchan by William Daniell 1816

The Island Lighthouses of Scotland

The rugged coastline of Scotland is about 6,000 miles long (18,588 km). It is peppered - especially along the west - by some 800 islands, only about 100 of which are now inhabited. Early charts were poor and it was only in 1800 that the Admiralty began to produce reliable sea charts: nowadays they are the envy of the world. At the same time a system of navigational aids began to be constructed around the coast. The Commissioners for Northern Lighthouses, or the Northern Lighthouse Board (NLB), was formed in 1786 becoming one of the first such authorities. It developed a distinguished history of lighthouse building resulting in this tiny country of ours becoming one of the best lit coasts anywhere. Today, throughout Scotland and the Isle of Man, the NLB operates no fewer than 208 lighthouses along with 160 buoys, 31 beacons, 27 radar beacons (RACONS), 26 Automatic Identification System (AIS) stations and 4 Differential Global Positioning System (DGPS) stations. Although more venerable, larger and maintaining nearly 600 aids to navigation in England and Wales, Trinity House is responsible for only 69 lighthouses.

Major lights are defined as beams with a range exceeding 15 miles, and in Scotland there are now about a hundred, with many more minor lights and buoys. Twenty five of these major lighthouses are to be found on the mainland coast.

The remainder are situated on islands. Lights had to be maintained so, initially, they were all designed to provide accommodation for keepers and, whether on or off station, for their families.

It was not until 1890 that unmanned lighthouses came to be constructed in Scotland. With development in kerosene lamps a programme of automation could begin, at first only involving smaller beacons and harbour lights. But, with improvements in range, Oxcars in the Firth of Forth became the first lighthouse to go automatic in 1894. A concerted, phased programme began in 1960 which was finally completed in 1998, with all major lighthouses now automated. It is these major lighthouses, formerly manned, that are the focus of this publication.

Some lighthouse stations were conveniently close to habitation, and most were – almost by definition – in remote situations. They were classified according to their situation and status. **Shore lighthouse stations** are situated on the mainland of Scotland where the lightkeepers' families lived in attached or adjacent dwelling houses. The men worked a five day working week with normal annual holidays. A few of these smaller lights were one-man operated since the technology no longer necessitated night watches. **Island lighthouse** stations were those built on offshore islands, often large ones and, similarly, the families were still able to live on site. So called **Relieving stations** could be situated on the mainland or larger inhabited islands but in such remote and inaccessible locations that it was considered unfair and impractical to expect the families to live there. Their accommodation might be situated some distance from the lighthouse, sometimes many miles away. **Rock lighthouses** were on small uninhabited islands, remote and barren rocks, reefs and skerries to which the keepers had to commute by boat or, latterly, by helicopter. At **Rock and Relieving stations** it was necessary to have a compliment of six keepers working a month on/month off, always with three men manning the lighthouse at any one time. The off duty keepers could be with their families on shore - although even here there was always work to be done.

Scotland has a proud tradition in lighthouse building, matched nowhere else in the world. This arose, through four or five generations, within one family – the Stevensons. As Engineers to the NLB they went on to influence lighthouse design right through to the present day. The family firm of marine engineers advised on the construction of lighthouses worldwide and were also responsible for countless beacons, harbours, breakwaters and bridges around Scotland. Yet it is indeed ironic that it should be the black sheep of the family who became the most famous – the writer Robert Louis Stevenson. He rebelled against a career in engineering, yet later would proudly write:

'Whenever I smell salt water, I know that I am not far from one of the works of my ancestors.'   Robert Louis Stevenson 1880

The need for lighted beacons as an aid to fishing vessels and shipping has been recognised since antiquity. One of the Seven Wonders of the Ancient World, the Pharos at Alexandria, was a lighthouse (and it is thought that the Colossus of Rhodes – built in 3000 BC - might have been another). The 142 metre tall Pharos of Alexandria was built between 283 and 247 BC at the harbour entrance and its beacon of fire was said to have been visible for 30 miles. Over the centuries it suffered from several earthquakes until finally collapsing in 1326. But its name, which actually came from the island upon which it stood, lives on. 'Pharology' is the study of lighthouses while, in 1807, one of the Northern Lighthouse Board's first ships was named *'Pharos'*. The tenth and current vessel of the same name came into service exactly 200 years later.

'Pharos' X with helicopter, Sound of Harris June 2011 (J Love)

In the first or second century AD the Romans built a lighthouse at Dover over-looking the English Channel, which still stands within the confines of the Castle. Later, some monasteries took it upon themselves to provide fire beacons as aids to navigation. One of the first was built in the fifth century at Hook Head in Co. Wexford, Eire. Part of this structure has been incorporated into later buildings so the current tower claims to be the oldest working lighthouse in the United

Kingdom. Monks on Heisgeir, or the Monach Isles, 4 miles west of North Uist, are also said to have maintained a beacon in the 5th century, perhaps the oldest known in Scotland. The current lighthouse stands on the westernmost and smallest now uninhabited island of Shillay. There is also a tradition that St Geradine displayed a lantern at Covesea on the Moray coast: he is incorporated into the coat of arms of Lossiemouth.

Shillay, one of the Monach Isles with lighthouse (A R Mainwood)

Around the sixteenth century mariners, ship owners and merchants formed themselves into brotherhoods, fraternities or guilds, which were effectively religious charities for the mutual help and welfare of seamen and their dependants. Called Trinity Houses three are known to have been set up in Scotland (Aberdeen, Dundee and Leith), with Dover, Hull and London's main port of Deptford on the Thames. The latter was possibly the oldest, dating perhaps from the 9th century and is the only one to have survived. By 1514 it became 'Trinity House' as we know it today. Although the organisation did build one or two lighthouses, it functioned mainly by encouraging speculation and issuing charters from the Crown to landowners and entrepreneurs enabling them to construct lighthouses around the coasts of England and Wales. Eventually mariners began to complain about extortionate fees so it was decided to bring them all under one unitary authority. Later still, an Act of 1836 enabled Trinity House to purchase the final 10 private lighthouses, the last being The Skerries off Anglesey , Wales (built 1714), which was bought for £444,984 – the most profitable and the most expensive!

From the Middle Ages, several North Sea ports in Scotland maintained a lively trade, exchanging salt fish, wool, hides and later, wheat, rye and malt, for fine cloth, flax and good wines. Leith, Dundee and Aberdeen were major centres of such commerce centred across the North Sea. Various sea-marks stood at harbour entrances for the benefit of such merchant vessels and also the local fishing fleets. Two beacons had been established at the mouth of Leith harbour by 1553, when one of them is recorded as having been damaged by an English ship! Another is known to have been in position at Aberdeen by 1566. Fifty years later, coal mining, salt production, fishing and the North Sea trade demanded further marks or beacons on 'all the craiges and blind rocks' within the Firth of Forth 'for the crydit of the country and saftie of strangers.'

Scotland's first lighthouse

By now merchants were actively petitioning the Crown for a lighthouse on the Isle of May. It is said that 10th century monks had kept a beacon burning there to guide voyagers on the pilgrims' way to the holy shrines at St Andrews. Charles I granted a patent to James Maxwell of Innerwick and John Cunninghame of Barnes to erect a beacon on the Isle of May in 1636, to become Scotland's first permanent lighthouse. All ships belonging to the kingdom of Scotland which sailed from or arrived at ports between Dunnottar Castle and St Abb's Head, were to pay 2 shillings Scots per ton, and 4 shillings for foreign ships (which for many years after the 1707 Union of Parliaments still included English ships!) The levies were collected at the ports for the proprietors of the island who, in turn, paid a commission to the Scottish crown.

The Isle of May lighthouse was built as an ornate three-storied tower 25 feet square and 40 feet high, with a coal-fired beacon on its roof. It consumed some 200 tons of coal every year, sometimes 3 tons on windy, winter nights. The lighthouse keeper had to carry the coals from the shore on his back. He and his family lived underneath the beacon, on a remuneration in 1786 of only £7 a year.

One night in January 1791 George Anderson, his wife and four children were overcome with fumes from the ash pile just outside. Only a baby survived who was brought up in Fife and when aged 16 Lucy Anderson married one of her rescuers, Henry Downie, 22 years her senior. They emigrated to North America. In 2004 (and again in 2009) her great, great, great, great grand-daughter from the US visited the Isle of May in pursuit of her family history. When the Isle of May tower finally came to be replaced by a new lighthouse in 1816, the NLB engineer Robert Stevenson proposed demolishing the original building. Fortunately, his friend Sir Walter Scott pleaded with him only to ruin it a là picturesque and so it remains to this day.

Original beacon on the Isle of May 1967 (J Love)

In 1687 two leading lights had come to be exhibited from Buddon Ness, at the mouth of the Firth of Tay near Dundee. A guiding light had been erected at Portpatrick around 1680 but the Act of Union 1707 opened up Atlantic trade routes into Scotland and, with Dumfries an important port at the time, a light was built at Southerness on the Solway in 1749. But it was the River Clyde that was determined to benefit. In 1756, as part of the on-going development of Irvine, then Port Glasgow and finally Glasgow itself, the Trustees of the Clyde Lights (the first statutory lighthouse authority) was established.

The Trustees erected a 28 foot high, coal-fired beacon was erected on Little Cumbrae the following year. This time the dues would be paid not to private individuals as at the Isle of May, or to a fraternity of sailors - as at Dundee - but to Trustees who would use them exclusively for the upkeep of the lights. Thus, for the first time, an authority was set up for the principal provision and maintenance of lighthouses. A new and viable precedent had been set, but by 1760 there were still only six lighthouses in Scotland. The golden age of lighthouse building in Scotland was undoubtedly the 19th century, but it is necessary first to consider a pioneering venture on the notorious Eddystone Rock, 14 miles south of Plymouth in the English Channel.

Great and Little Cumbrae at the entrance of the River Clyde (J Love)

Old print of the original beacon on Little Cumbrae

The Eddystone lighthouse – daring and original

During the seventeenth century there was widespread pressure for a beacon to be built on dangerous rocks of Eddystone. At that time there was no such thing as a marine engineer but a flamboyant and eccentric entrepreneur took it upon himself to erect the lighthouse. No one had ever attempted such a project before, to build on a rock only a metre of which was ever exposed at high tide, but Henry Winstanley (1644-1703) rose to the task.

Almost at once, Winstanley had to modify his original structure until in 1698 the tallow candles atop this bizarre, ornate tower, 37 metres tall (including sundry appendages) were finally lit. *'It is finished,'* he wrote, *' and it will stand forever as one of the world's most artistic pieces of work.'* Unfortunately this was never to be for, only five years later on 26 Nov 1703, his tower, with him and his lightkeepers inside, were washed away in a terrible storm. As long as Winstanley's light had shone no more ships had foundered on Eddystone but within two days the *Winchelsea*, disabled in the storm, hit the rock and went down with all but two of its 69 hands. Having come to rely upon Winstanley's beacon mariners were once again in danger, so a replacement became a matter of urgency.

John Rudyerd (1650- 1718), a silk merchant with practical bent, came forward having sought advice and co-operation from naval shipwrights. In 1708, just four and half years after the loss of Winstanley's tower, Rudyerd's builders had erected his elegant 'conical ship', firstly of stone blocks keyed into the parent rock, then stout seasoned timbers bound with iron bands, all clad in hardwood panels caulked with oakum and coated in pitch. The structure demanded considerable and costly annual maintenance but endured for nigh on half a century before its fatal weakness was exposed – fire.

The man charged with another replacement lighthouse was a Leeds instrument maker and mathematician known to have a flair for civil and mechanical engineering problems, John Smeaton (1724 – 92). With characteristic forethought he quickly realised that the shape best suited to withstanding the mighty forces of the sea resembled the flared trunk of an oak tree. The material needed was nothing less than pure stone, an interlocking structure of variously hewn blocks assembled like a three-dimensional jigsaw, further bound together with oak pins or trenails and held with a quick-setting marine cement of his own devising. The building, at 22 metres similar in height to Rudyerd's, had been completed by 1759 without loss of life. Smeaton had finally tamed the Eddystone Rock and his innovative methods were to remain standard in lighthouse construction across various parts of the world for 250 years.

Smeaton's tower re-erected on Plymouth Hoe (J Love)

In the end it was not his famous tower that failed but the eroding rock upon which it stood. But it was not until 1879 that work began on a replacement, to be designed by Sir James Nicholas Douglass (1826 – 98), Engineer-in-Chief to Trinity House. His task demanded building on a neighbouring rock which was covered at all states of the tide. This fifth Eddystone tower employed many structural features pioneered by Smeaton, and indeed later by Robert Stevenson, and proved both functional and elegant. It was automated in 1982, exactly 100 years after its completion, with the addition of a helicopter landing pad its roof on.

But the good and grateful people of Plymouth were not to forget the efforts of John Smeaton. In 1884 they had raised sufficient funds for his redundant lighthouse to be dismantled from Eddystone and re-erected for all to admire on Plymouth Hoe. Only a stump remains at sea.

Douglas's Eddystone with the stump of Smeaton's tower (Chantal Cookson)

Thomas Smith and the first NLB lighthouses

Towards the end of the century fishing, trade and travel had greatly increased shipping in Scottish waters. All vessels between the Clyde and Baltic ports for instance had to sail round the north of Scotland. An unprecedented succession of storms in 1782 highlighted the dangers so, as Trinity House had no jurisdiction over Scotland, an Act of Parliament was quickly passed in 1786 to establish the Commissioners for Northern Lighthouses (later the Northern Lighthouse Board or NLB) in Edinburgh. It was probably the first authority in the world with the sole duty of managing lighthouses on a national scale. In 1815 the Isle of Man recognised their expertise and opted to become affiliated to the NLB rather than Trinity House.

The Commissioners were not selected for their maritime experience but made up a curious panel consisting of two Crown Officers for Scotland, the Lord Advocate and Solicitor-General, the Lord Provosts of Edinburgh and Glasgow, the Provosts of Aberdeen, Inverness and Campbelltown, and the Sheriffs of certain maritime counties. Nonetheless, in order *'to conduce greatly to the security of navigation'* they quickly authorised the building of four new lighthouses at strategic headlands around the north of Scotland – Kinnaird Head in Buchan and the easternmost extremity of the Scottish mainland, North Ronaldsay the northern tip of Orkney, Scalpay on Harris in the Minch, and the Mull of Kintyre between Scotland and Ireland. As Engineer to undertake this task they appointed a lamp-maker called Thomas Smith (1752 – 1814) - an *'ingenious and modest . . . tin plate worker'*

On the small clifftop at Kinnaird Head the very first lantern was placed on the roof of a redundant 16th century castle, a task supervised by Smith himself to the design of an Edinburgh architect Alexander Kay. Lit on 1st December 1787 it was the most powerful light of its time, with 17 oil lamps with reflectors arranged in 3 tiers.

Kinnaird Head lighthouse (W Daniell 1816)

One of Thomas Smith's reflectors (J Love)

Kinnaird Head, Fraserburgh, now the Scottish Lighthouse Museum (J Love)

The Mull of Kintyre presented more of a challenge, all the materials having to be hauled overland by pack horses a distance of 12 miles to the site, 90 metres above the sea. The station was rebuilt in the early 1800s until automated in 1996.

Eilean Glas on the island of Scalpay, Harris was the first lighthouse to be built in the Outer Hebrides. It is said that a torch beacon has been maintained here in the 15th century and of course, long before, a beacon had been maintained by monks on the Monach Isles. North Ronaldsay built on a low, flat island necessitated a 70 ft tower; it was lit in October 1789. Although the Scalpay lightroom was about 73 ft above sea level, wave action demanded the deployment of especially thick glass panes. And so the light was eventually exhibited, along with that on Ronaldsay, in October 1789.

Eilean Glas, Scalpay, Isle of Harris (W Daniell 1816)

Once built these lighthouses had to be manned. Robert Louis Stevenson recorded how:

'A whole service, with its routine and hierarchy, had to be called out of nothing; and a new trade, that of lightkeeper, to be taught, recruited and organised.'

The first NLB lightkeeper, appointed on a wage of £30 a year with a garden, pasture for a cow and enough fuel for domestic use, was James Park at Kinnaird Head, a former ship's master. He retired due to ill health 9 years later, aged

80. Matthew Harvie stationed at Kintyre was a local man, the first of a line of lightkeepers whose family had for some years before kept a light burning in the kitchen window of their croft to warn seamen off the rocks. But at North Ronaldsay another former shipmaster had soon to be dismissed after embezzling the stores. At Scalpay in contrast, the first lightkeeper Alexander Reid was ultimately pensioned off after no less than 34 years' service.

Developments continued in the Firth of Clyde, for the benefit of Glasgow. Merchants continued dredging and realigning the river enabling ships to sail right into the heart of what would become the second greatest city of the British Empire. The next lighthouse recommended in the 1786 Act was on the island of Pladda, off the southeast corner of Arran which was lit in 1790. But it required to be distinguished from the fixed lights at the Mull of Kintyre, on Cumbrae and at Copeland on the Irish coast. So a lower light 20 feet below the main one was added, a system that was to operate for 100 years.

The double light on Pladda, south of Arran (J Love)

Meanwhile it had become evident that the hilltop, coal-fired beacon on Cumbrae was often obscured by cloud or mist and, since the Pladda light was considered by local mariners to be *'the best light they knew of anywhere'*, all agreed that Cumbrae would be improved by conversion to oil lamps. Smith sent his assistant Robert Stevenson to supervise construction of a new lighthouse on the shore, which was lit in October 1793. It was also felt that another lighthouse was needed on the Clyde, at Cloch Point. Thomas Smith added the lantern, with young Stevenson's help, and which was lit in August 1797. By now Smith had also converted Buddon Ness from coal to oil.

There was also a plan to open up the Pentland Firth known as 'Hell's Mouth' rather than the longer route round the north of Orkney; but it was a notorious passage. Another double light, similar to Pladda, was erected on the Pentland Skerries in 1794; the two towers 80 and 60 feet high and 60 feet apart. Built by Orkney masons they were supervised by Robert Stevenson, his first official work for the NLB.

The double light on the Pentland Skerries, Orkney (J Love)

19

Light dues had brought the newly-fledged NLB an income of £1,477 in 1790 but by 1802 this had risen to £4,386 encouraging them to consider new lights. The island and rocks of Inchkeith in the Firth of Forth had always presented a hazard to ships entering the naval port of Leith so Stevenson identified a suitable site for a lighthouse on an old Mary, Queen of Scots fort dating from 1564. Inchkeith came to be exhibited in September 1804 with Stevenson incorporating reflectors of silver-plated copper instead of his mentor's old mirror-glass. A plaque on the handsome tower and accommodation block credits Thomas Smith as being the engineer. Notwithstanding, Robert was now effectively running the lighthouse side of the business, having been made a full partner in 1800.

An unlit tower of masonry had been built as a seamark on Sanday, Orkney in 1802. But when a new light was proposed at Start Point on the same island it was at first resented by the penurious community as it might interfere with the plunder they gleaned from all the wrecks in the vicinity. For a time this tower came to replace North Ronaldsay altogether. A stone ball from the original tower on Start Point (now classified as an historic monument) was placed atop the redundant structure on North Ronaldsay. It would not be until 1854 that the present tall and elegant, brick-built tower came to be built alongside – at 42 m with 176 steps the tallest land-based lighthouse in UK.

The old tower (being restored) and modern lighthouse,
North Ronaldsay, Orkney (J Love)

20

In 1806 Start Point (with its unique and distinctive black vertical stripe not added until 1915) was to exhibit Scotland's first revolving light. Indeed Stevenson had wanted to employ this innovation on Pentland Skerries some years earlier, being a cheaper method of distinguishing different lighthouse beams and obviating the need for two separate towers. On a tour of English lights in 1801 he had been impressed by St Agnes in the Scillies and by Cromer where the reflector frames revolved by clockwork *'exhibiting a brilliant light once in every minute'*.

Operations were now so widespread that Thomas Smith, as NLB Engineer, had to undertake annual inspections by sea. This tradition was to impose gruelling physical demands on Smith and his successors. At this time too, Britain was at war with France and Smith came close to being captured by a French squadron. Press gangs from the Royal Navy were another hazard, in addition to the accepted risks negotiating dangerous waters and storms. After completing his work at Pentland Skerries for instance, Stevenson sailed south in a Stromness sloop *Elizabeth* but bad weather necessitated him landing near Kinnaird Head to continue overland to Edinburgh. Returning northwards the *Elizabeth* was then lost with all hands. From 1797 Stevenson became responsible for all the NLB inspection voyages.

Robert Stevenson

Thomas Smith (1752-1815) had been widowed twice and had surviving children. With his business expanding and demanding more time away from home, his kindly neighbour Jean (sometimes called Jane) Stevenson neé Lillie (1751-1820), who had been a friend to both his wives, offered to help look after his children. They married in 1787 and Smith hired her 19 year old son Robert Stevenson (1772-1850) as his apprentice.

Robert had grown up with Thomas Smith's children and was to marry his daughter Jane (1779-1846) in 1799. She was 20 and he 27, soon to be made a full partner in his step-father's business. In 1808 Thomas Smith finally relinquished his post as NLB Engineer to his stepson. He died in 1815 having constructed ten lighthouses for the Northern Lighthouse Board. Robert and Jane were to have 13 children but only five survived – Jane, Alan, Robert, David and Thomas.

The Bell Rock

Eleven miles out from Arbroath, and over 300 metres long, lies the most feared hazard to shipping on the east coast of Scotland - Inchcape Rock. At high tide it lies under up to five metres of water and only a metre ever shows above the sea. Someone calculated it wrecked up to half a dozen ships every winter.

Legend has it that in the 14th century the Abbot of Arbroath fixed a bell to

Inchcape which rung to the motion of the wind and waves to warn mariners of impending danger. The story goes that a pirate called Ralph the Rover, who had long profited from the wrecks, tore down the bell, and famously perished upon the rock. Thus this notorious place became known as the Bell Rock.

The Commissioners of Northern Lights were well aware of the hazard but at a loss to know how to deal with it. They had considered the project in the 1790s but opted to build Pentland Skerries instead. During storms in December 1799 over 70 ships foundered along the Scottish coast, two of them on the Bell Rock so the Commissioners had to act. This time they instructed Robert Stevenson to survey the rock. Stevenson had first looked at Bell Rock in the summer of 1794 and, on his first landing in October 1800, he confessed:

'I am sure no one was fonder of his own work than I was until I saw the Bell Rock.'

In January 1804 HMS *York* was lost with all hands at the Bell Rock. Several floating buoys were installed over the reef but none survived the winter storms. Passing the Bell Rock from time to time, had not lessened Stevenson's resolve. In 1803 he pondered:

'The more I see of the Rock the less I think of the difficulty I at first conceived of erecting a building of stone upon it.'

He remained convinced that only a stout stone structure similar to that devised by John Smeaton for Eddystone in the English Channel was required, the work-force being accommodated on temporary barracks erected alongside. Since none of the rock showed above the high tide however there would be additional technical challenges never faced by Smeaton.

Bell Rock and the Angus coast at sunset (J Love)

The NLB had considered 35 year old Stevenson still to be lacking in experience to undertake this monumental task. So in 1806 they agreed that he should work as Assistant alongside a recognised engineer John Rennie. In the end Stevenson was not only left to his own devices, but was able to ignore many of Rennie's recommendations. Whatever Rennie's role, history now records Robert Stevenson as the builder of the Bell Rock lighthouse. Indeed so impressed were the NLB by Stevenson's abilities they accepted him as their Chief Engineer in 1808 (a post he retained until 1843).

The author at the Bell Rock, June 2010 (J Love)

After Bell Rock

Thomas Smith died four years later, in 1815. With Bell Rock, Robert Stevenson's reputation was now firmly established and his career, and business, flourished. It would never be challenged again, and his subsequent commissions might now seem somewhat mundane, many of them on the mainland. In 1816 he was commissioned to replace the old coal beacon on the Isle of May. His stately lighthouse block became fully automatic in 1989, ending a proud tally of 353 years operation by light keepers!

The new lighthouse, Isle of May (J Love)

The Isle of May with the Low Light, the old beacon,
the new light and foghorn (J Love)

By now the NLB were operating 16 major lights (including two on the Isle of Man) and the momentum was still growing. In 1821, during his annual inspection cruise in the yacht *Regent*, Robert Stevenson visited Eilean Glas lighthouse in Harris. The Scalpay factor presented him with a live great auk which some St Kilda men had caught three years previously. The intention was to keep the flightless great auk alive as long as possible and then present its body to the Edinburgh University Museum. However, after Stevenson had left the ship, the bird made its escape near the entrance to the Firth of Clyde. This was one of the last of its kind; and, before Robert Stevenson himself ended his days, the great auk would be extinct.

Stevenson's lighthouse work continued, with the completion in 1821 of Sumburgh Head at the southernmost tip of Shetland. In 1825 the Rinns of Islay light was erected on the small tidal Isle of Orsay across from Portnahaven. Seven more mainland lighthouses followed and in 1828 Robert Stevenson embarked upon the lighthouse at Cape Wrath, the most north-westerly tip of the Scottish mainland. A third Manx light was constructed in 1832 while Robert was simultaneously completing Lismore light in the Sound of Mull, at the entrance to Loch Linnhe -the gateway to the Caledonian Canal. This light was first exhibited in October 1833 with Robert Selkirk, a descendant of Alexander Selkirk ('Robinson Crusoe'), as its first Principal Lightkeeper.

Lismore Lighthouse, Sound of Mull (J Love)

Barra Head – Robert's final challenge

Robert Stevenson's final major challenge was Barra Head, on the island of Berneray at the southernmost tip of the Outer Hebrides. He had visited the place on his inspection voyage of 1828 accompanied by his 13 year old son. The site chosen was one and a half miles from the landing place, on the highest point. An Iron Age fort was partially destroyed during the building of the lighthouse but it remains an impressive structure. Robert Stevenson began construction in 1830 and wrote:

'Such is the violence of the wind in this station that the temporary buildings occupied by the artificers were repeatedly unroofed. On the face of the precipitous cliffs the winds and seas acquire a force which the reporter has never experienced elsewhere . . . The artificers are often reduced to the necessity of passing the most exposed places on their knees clinging with their hands to the ground . . . In one of these storms the lighthouse cart and horse overturned by the force of the wind. . . It is remarkable that the horse sustained no injury.'

Barra Head with its lighthouse
(J Love)

Barra Head lighthouse, Berneray,
Outer Hebrides (J Love)

The stone tower is only 18 metres high, but the light is about 250 metres above sea level and in clear weather had a range of 18 miles. The last native islanders were to quit around 1910 leaving only lighthouse families until a shore station was established for them in Oban, 85 miles away. On 23 October 1980 Barra Head Lighthouse was converted to automatic operation and the lightkeepers withdrawn.

Alan Stevenson

Robert Stevenson ran the Lighthouse Service along military lines and brought up his sons with a similar degree of discipline. Having come from a poor background he saw engineering as an appropriate and prosperous career. Only young Robert (Bob) managed to escape by becoming a surgeon in the Army. Alan (1807 – 65) the eldest son, although not physically strong and with a distinct classical bent, was of course pressurised to take up engineering. At 12 years of age Alan began his apprenticeship on an inspection voyage with his father, along with his younger siblings Jane and Bob and their two Smith cousins. Three years later Alan's apprentice status was formalised and in 1824 he really began to cut his teeth by assisting his father with the Rinns of Islay.

Mull of Kintyre 1983 (J Love)

For a long time Robert had championed reflectors until Alan brought him round to the Fresnel lenses he had seen in France. Lighthouses could look quite distinctive in daylight but distinguishing them at night had always presented a problem. Robert had used two adjacent lights and red glass but now father and son saw the possibilities in Fresnel's flashing lights and lamps revolving behind a screen, Operated by clockwork, winding up the mechanism every 20 minutes or so was a principal duty of lightkeepers – and helped keep them awake! Since it was so convenient to Edinburgh, the lighthouse on Inchkeith, off Leith, was usually used to test new developments.

Inchkeith off Leith in the Firth of Forth (J Love)

With Robert now heavily engaged in designing bridges, harbours and river works as well as lighthouses, Alan took a bigger role for the Lighthouse Board, for whom he was appointed Clerk of Works in 1830 – a post his father had held 25 years earlier. It was around this time that the NLB moved into 84 George Street in Edinburgh, where it remains to this day. Robert Stevenson's family firm moved into the floor above them and Robert finally retired from the NLB in 1843, at the age of 70. After the death of his wife Jane three years later he also retired from the family firm. Robert died on 12th July 1850, Alan saying of him:

'*A high sense of duty pervaded his whole life and he died calmly . . .*'

Skerryvore – the noblest of all

Eleven miles south of Tiree lay a treacherous eight mile long reef, called Skerryvore. Between 1790 and 1844 over 30 ships had foundered there. In 1804 Robert Stevenson had managed to land upon the reef and took every opportunity to view it thereafter. Ten years later Sir Walter Scott concluded:

'A most desolate position for a lighthouse – the Bell Rock and Eddystone a joke to it.'

In 1834 the NLB finally took the decision to illuminate Skerryvore but - now getting on in years - Robert entrusted this to his 27 year old son Alan. He was 8 years younger than his father had been when, with some reluctance, the NLB had entrusted Robert to take on the Bell Rock. Alan reflected on the task:

'From the great difficulty of access to the inhospitable rock of Skerryvore, which is exposed to the full fury of the Atlantic, and is surrounded by an almost perpetual surf, the erection of a Light on its small and rugged surface has always been regarded as an undertaking of the most formidable kind.'

The sailing vessel *Pharos*, veteran of Bell Rock days, was again brought into service until a steam tender was ready. Again, like Eddystone and Bell Rock, the situation demanded a stone tower of interlocking blocks (up to 2½ tons in weight). But Skerryvore rock was more extensive, difficult to approach and lay open to the full fetch of the Atlantic Ocean. Furthermore, the nearest land was not the mainland but Tiree, an island in the Inner Hebrides. An elaborate shore station and harbour was established at Hynish in Tiree with stone for the tower being sourced from a quarry on Earraid in Mull further east. A channel had to be found to facilitate access on to the reef, while negotiating the slippery, polished rock was likened to climbing the neck of a bottle. The first barrack built on the rock did not survive its first winter so had to be rebuilt before work could start again. The foundation pit for the tower, sunk into hard gneiss rock, necessitated the use of dynamite. Considering the confines of the reef it is a wonder that no one was seriously hurt. The whole project would take seven years - much of Alan's career - and (including the Hynish facility with its keepers' family accommodation) cost £86,977.17s.7d.

Alan had proposed a taller tower than Bell Rock, at 48 m high with an enormous flared base 14 m in diameter. Altogether 4,300 tons of granite were employed, twice as much as Bell Rock and 4½ times as much as Smeaton's Eddystone . Furthermore Alan had taken the bold decision to save time and money by only interlocking the blocks horizontally, relying on the weight of the structure and mortar to bind each storey vertically. This resulted in the structure yielding somewhat to the pounding of the waves. Many years later one lighthouse keeper confidently observed how Skerryvore would yield slightly in storms while the Bell Rock would shudder on impact.

Alan's youngest brother Thomas, fast developing a skill with Fresnel lenses, helped install the lantern - Skerryvore's 'crown of glittering glass'. Skerryvore was finally exhibited on 1 February 1844. The light could be seen from Barra 38 miles to the west, and, allegedly, from the summit of Ben Nevis 90 miles east. The resulting tower, Robert Louis Stevenson judged, was:

'The noblest of all extant deep-sea lights.'

Old print of Skerryvore (left) and the Stevenson optic in the National Museums of Scotland, Edinburgh (J Love)

Some even claim Skerryvore to be the most elegant lighthouse in the world. At 48 metres it remains the tallest lighthouse in Scotland. (The tallest in the UK is Bishop Rock, redesigned by William Tregarthen Douglass, son of Sir James who had built last Eddystone Lighthouse, is now 49 m tall, having lost 2 metres when a helipad was established on its roof).

In 1892 the lighthouse families were moved from Hynish in Tiree to Erraid, until finally being accommodated in Oban. The lighthouse became automatic in 1994.

Skerryvore on the horizon (J Love)

After Skerryvore

With Skerryvore Alan had risen to a challenge that some say exceeds that of his father. Robert had finally relinquished his NLB Chief Engineer post to Alan in 1843 but all that happened was that Alan continued as Clerk of Works as well.

With 30 lighthouses now on the NLB books Alan began to suffer from the pressure of work. In May 1844 for example, he left Edinburgh for Inverness, a coach journey of 20 hours. Next morning he visited Cromarty and Fortrose, then Chanonry from where he was rowed to Inverness, continued to Forres where he spent the Sabbath (a day of rest for the Stevenson family) before visiting Covesea Skerries, then Fraserburgh via Elgin and Banff. He inspected Kinnaird lighthouse then Peterhead harbour, Buchan Ness and Girdleness before returning home via Dundee – all in the space of 8 days! This was just one of several such trips that year, which also included the annual inspection voyage in July and a trip to the Isle of Man, where he received a ducking landing at the Calf of Man and then another at Cape Wrath a few days later. He had never enjoyed a robust constitution and soon afterwards began to suffer from lumbago.

With this punishing routine Alan completed lighthouses at Covesea, Chanonry, Noss Head and Ardnamurchan, the latter lit in 1849. He then went on to tackle Sanda (1850) situated off the south end of Kintyre. Alan set two curious stone towers against the face of the rock, to enclose access between the accommodation block and the light tower on top of the rock; a unique design in Scotland. This resulted in an NLB overspend for 1848 and Sanda was first lighted in 1850.

Although none of Alan's subsequent lights were to prove quite as challenging as Skerryvore, they were nonetheless demanding enough of his time and energies that he took on an assistant, Alan Brebner, the son of his father's mason on Bell Rock. In 1851 Alan built both Hoy High and Hoy Low as leading lights for the famous naval anchorage of Scapa Flow, in Orkney, followed by Arnish in Lewis in 1853.

Arnish, at the entrance to Stornoway harbour, is noteworthy for it is here that Thomas Stevenson was able to test his latest innovation – the 'apparent light'. Seamen had long lamented that many seamarks were unlit – both 'blind' and 'dumb' they said. Thomas came up with the idea of using the beam from a nearby lighthouse to bounce off glass prisms mounted on the seamark. The deception was to prove so perfect that *'fishermen will not believe that there is not a light there.'* Arnish was chosen as the first site to showcase this device which was to remain in operation for fifty years. Finally worn out the buoy had to be replaced in 1905, but this time was lit by gas.

*Arnish lighthouse, Stornoway, Isle of Lewis with a modern buoy where
Thomas Stevenson erected his 'apparent light' (J Love)*

Alan was a remarkable engineer not only recognised at home, but also abroad with an invitation to design a lighthouse for Singapore. He had always retained a love of the arts; fluent in Latin, Greek, French, Spanish and Italian he translated and memorised Greek poetry. Indeed it is a characteristic of his lighthouse architecture that he incorporated discrete Classical and Egyptian influences, Ardnamurchan being a notable example.

Alan retired prematurely in 1853 due to ill health. With no pension, he died in somewhat reduced circumstances in 1865. He had pushed himself to his absolute limits and in the short time allotted to him was responsible for 12 major lighthouses in a ten- year career as NLB Chief Engineer. His father had achieved 20 in a 44 year career. Just as Bell Rock was his father's, Skerryvore will always be Alan's memorial which his peers recognised as:

'. . . a triumph of lighthouse engineering, and as perhaps the finest combination of mass with elegance to be met with in architectural engineering.'

The Golden Years

During Alan's tenure with the NLB his younger brother David Stevenson (1815 – 86) had built a reputation for the firm in river engineering, while Thomas (1818 – 87), the youngest, had particular skills in optics, invention and science. On Alan's retirement, David took over the role as Chief Engineer with the NLB but soon convinced the Commissioners to make this a joint position with Thomas. Nine new lighthouses were already on the drawing board, dozens of beacons and buoys besides a mountain of associated paperwork. Not in the best of health, David presided over what might be termed the "Golden Years" of lighthouse construction. The two brothers made a fine team but were as different as chalk and cheese. David was small, bespectacled, dapper, popular, reliable and addicted to work. He was the better engineer and a gifted manager within the family business. Thomas, on the other hand, was tall, quiet, stern, melancholic with rather strange and unconventional views but nonetheless able enough and dedicated when necessary.

Thomas was the youngest of Robert Stevenson's sons and initially, much to his father's annoyance, he showed little interest in the family business, being more interested in book collecting, literature and natural history. Robert once chastised Thomas when he found some manuscript pages of fiction in a drawer. He was urged to *give up such nonsense and mind your business.*' With little option Thomas took up engineering and proved quite inventive, particularly in the field of optics. Tom, for instance, assumed the major role in the final installation of the Dubh Artach light. After his brother David retired, Thomas would take over the family business. Amongst many diverse interests, Thomas will always be remembered as the inventor of the 'Stevenson's Screen' used in meteorological recording.

In 1848 Thomas married Margaret Isabella Balfour. Two years later, just months after his own father Robert Stevenson had died, Thomas's only child Robert Louis was born. Given his own upbringing, it is strange that Thomas should prove so exasperated by his own rebellious son's literary ambitions, concluding writing to be '*no profession*'. Notwithstanding father and son would later enjoy corresponding over literary matters and even correct each other's writings and speeches. Bella Bathurst analysed the complexities of Thomas's character – '*a man forever fighting his own contradictions*'.

It is unfortunate perhaps that David's individual achievements are always considered in conjunction with those of his brother. Around 1870, for instance, David famously promoted the use of paraffin in lighthouses. The earliest beacons in Britain had burnt solid fuel, mostly coal. Around 1750 21 of the 25 navigation lights in Britain, nearly all of them in England, were still coal-fired. This was a convenient fuel, burning longer than wood in wet weather. Coal did however burn three times faster in windy weather, demanded constant and laborious attendance, but worst of all ships could easily be confuse coal beacons with domestic or industrial fires ashore.

By the early 1800s Arctic whaling was a major industry in Scotland, from ports such as Dundee, Peterhead and the Northern Isles. The first new Argand lamp, using silver-plated copper reflectors, and fuelled with sperm oil, was installed in Inchkeith. In 1804 crude whale oil or the finer spermaceti then became the main illuminant for oil lamps in many early Scottish lighthouses. Whale oil lamps needed modification in order to be replaced by cleaner colza (produced from oil-seed rape). But both the quality and supply of colza proved erratic, not to mention its increasing cost. Other oils were tried – olive, seal, even herring – until, by 1847, shale oil from the Lothians became readily available. It was trialled in Girdleness lighthouse near Aberdeen, and first installed shortly afterwards at Pentland Skerries and Pladda. Paraffin could be extracted from mineral oil and became cheaper. Oil lamps then came to be superceded by bright mantles burning paraffin vapourised under pressure. It was this innovation that David Stevenson promoted so actively. In 1872 Dubh Artach had become the first rock light to utilise paraffin.

Northern Lights

By the mid-nineteenth century British trade was expanding and steamships were becoming commoner. The Board of Trade were the government body handling all things mercantile and wished to rationalise lighthouse administration in

Scotland, England and Ireland. The Merchant Shipping Act of 1853 accorded Trinity House more power over the NLB and the Irish Board. Regular wreck reports were initiated at this time too revealing how, between 1859 and 1866 there were an average of 24 vessels coming to grief every year around the Scottish coast. In 1853, when David Stevenson succeeded his brother Alan as NLB Engineer, he was already engaged in building a light at Davaar near Campbelltown and several lighthouses in Shetland, notably Muckle Flugga – 'the impossible light' on Britain's most northerly point.

Muckle Flugga – the impossible light

In 1850 Alan Stevenson had, with some difficulty, leapt ashore to snatch a rock specimen from Muckle Flugga's jagged outcrop, right in the path of North Atlantic storms. In February 1854 David Stevenson was despatched there to investigate and, unable to land, he deemed it impracticable to attempt anything. He was:

'. . .adamant that the seas around the Shetland coast made building a lighthouse in the area impossible, impractical, dangerous, too expensive, and any ship that took that route was mad anyway. . . [It would be] culpable recklessness as regards the lives of the lightkeepers to erect even a temporary lighthouse on the Flugga.'

David Stevenson favoured one of three other possibilities, especially Lamba Ness to the north east. Trinity House persisted however and when their own team managed to land without any difficulty on an unbelievably calm June day, they convinced both themselves and the Board of Trade. Stevenson reluctantly capitulated and in July his brother Thomas and Alan Brebner made the difficult climb to the summit of the Flugga and found a flat shelf that could accommodate at least a temporary light. Work had to begin immediately, and it took only 26 days to erect the temporary light which was first exhibited on 11 October 1854. A foreman Charles Barclay, who had lost a hand working at Skerryvore and a veteran of Barra Head, stayed overwinter to supervise cutting steps and maintain the light, reported 'sheet of white water' regularly driven 15 metres over the lantern. On one December morning:

'. . . the sea was all like smoke as far as we could see and the noise which the wind made on the roof of our house and on the tower was like thunder.'

The massive iron door of their temporary dwelling smashed open and admitted a metre high wall of water which swirled around inside before retreating along with everything that had not been tied down. This was followed by another, and then a third, before the men could secure the door again. All this nearly 70 metres above sea level, higher than Nelson's Column in Trafalgar Square! In June 1855, knowing that everything had to be man-handled up the rock, David Stevenson was forced to adopt *'an untried experiment in marine engineering'* – he would build his 20 metre high tower of bricks. Over 100 men worked on this unlikely site before a permanent light was exhibited on 1 January 1858.

The brick lighthouse on Muckle Flugga, Shetland (J Love)

Despite many storms of seismic fury the structure has stood, the sea never penetrated the tower and the light never failed. At 61° 59' N with only 5 hours 8 minutes operation required in midsummer - 'simmer dim' as the Shetlanders call it - the light burnt 1 gallon of paraffin per night; in midwinter on the other hand 3 gallons were needed over 18 hours 11 minutes.

The supply boats from the shore station at Burrafirth had their work cut out, especially in winter when relief might be delayed for 20 days or more. The advent of helicopters greatly facilitated this operation until the lighthouse was automated in 1995.

Skye Lights

Surprisingly, up to the middle of the 19th century, Skye had not figured in any plans to illuminate Scotland's shores. It was the advent of steamships, more manoeuvrable than sail, that opened up the Inner Sound east of Skye as a safe and sheltered sea route. Thus lighthouses were proposed at Kyleakin, Isle Ornsay and South Rona. All three were constructed by David and Thomas Stevenson and lighted on 10 November 1857. They bear the familiar lines of a Stevenson lighthouse but both Ornsay and Kyleakin came to incorporate another ingenious innovation of Thomas's. With the famous optical firm of Chance Brothers in Birmingham, he had developed a 'condensing' system of prisms that reduced the intensity of the beam in some directions whilst optimising it in others, ideal for narrow channels. From the handsome 19 metre high tower of Isle Ornsay for instance the light could shine brightest down the Sound of Sleat, less so northwards to Kylerhea, and dimmest of all directly across the narrows from the lighthouse itself.

Thomas Stevenson's condensing system from Isle Ornsay (National Museum of Scotland)

But perhaps Thomas Stevenson's greatest contribution to lighthouse optics was his development of the holophotal system. This ingenious device combined the whole sphere of rays diverging from a light source into a single beam of parallel rays. It was first adopted on a large scale at North Ronaldsay in 1851 and thereafter became universal throughout the service.

On South Rona a widow named Janet Mackenzie had maintained a light in her window so that local fishing boats would avoid dangerous rocks at the harbour entrance. For her "praiseworthy exertions" Alan Stevenson advised the NLB to reward her with £20.

One lighthouse keeper David Dunnet, the first of four generations in the service, was Principal at South Rona for no less than 16 years – 1878-95 - quite a tour of duty. All three lighthouses built along the Inner Sound had accommodation for three lighthouse keepers and their families but when Kyleakin and Ornsay were converted to gas in 1898 only one keeper was required.

Kyleakin lighthouse (now disused) under the Skye Bridge (J Love)

Kyleakin was fully automated in 1960 followed two years later by Ornsay. In 1963 both redundant accommodation blocks were sold to the author Gavin Maxwell who envisaged renting out Ornsay. In the end he had to sell Ornsay and only lived at Eilean Ban for a year or so until his death in 1969. The light was finally decommissioned in 1993 when the Skye Bridge opened above it. The house, said to have been haunted, has been restored and the island bought by the Eilean Ban Wildlife Trust. Later, David Stevenson's sons David A. and Charles would end their careers in 1934 with the construction of a minor light at Sleat Point on Skye, Tor Ness in Orkney and Rubh Uisenis in Lewis.

Political lighthouses

During the latter half of the nineteenth century, the tense liaison between the Board, Trinity House and the Commissioners continued. They argued over details, for instance, in the construction of Rubha nan Gall in the Sound of Mull for instance, on Skeirvule in the Sound of Jura, the Butt of Lewis, and Ruvaal on the Sound of Islay.

Rueval, Sound of Islay (J Love)

In 1859 a Royal Commission cruised round Britain and Ireland to report on lighthouses. One of its members, Captain, later Admiral Sir James Sullivan was particularly damning. He criticised the ignorant landsmen of the NLB for favouring cheaper inshore sites instead of the 'outer rocks'. Yet he was happy then to contradict himself; after praising the Stevensons' construction as *'very beautiful and the work never wants repair'* he went on to complain how they were *'more like gentleman's houses inside than lightkeepers' houses need be.'* Not content with that, he immediately criticised the Ruvaal accommodation as *'little better than dog kennels than anything else'* and was astonished that any human being could be got to live in them. The keepers observed how the light tower would oscillate in high winds, largely because of Board of Trade interference, an attitude the Royal Commission noted as keeping *'economy rather than progress in view'*. In the end the Commission concluded:

'As matters now stand, the whole management of the lighthouse service appears to be impeded by the opposing action of three separate governing bodies, and it does not clearly appear to what advantage is gained to counterbalance the delay which results from this complicated system... There can be no doubt that of all the British lighthouses visited, the Scotch are in the best state of general efficiency, the English next, and the Irish third.'

The report was finally published in 1861 – and totally failed to ignite any serious reforms. Happily the NLB was to retain some sort of autonomy, having opposed any form of centralisation from the outset. During this turbulent episode the NLB managed to exhibit the five lights sanctioned by the Board of Trade – Rubha nan Gall, Ornsay, Kyleakin, South Rona and Ushenish on South Uist – all on 10th November 1857.

Two other major lights were to incorporate Board of Trade economies. The Butt of Lewis (1862) was built of brick, by John Barr & Co of Ardrossan but it had been late in the year 1859 before the materials reached the Butt: the vessel was

Butt of Lewis, Outer Hebrides (J Love)

wrecked whilst unloading its cargo. Thus when the Commissioners visited on 23 July 1860 they found *'work not so far advanced as had been anticipated.'* Then the mason employed to build the 168 steps up the 37 m tower went on strike until he got an extra penny a day. Supplies continued to be brought by boat to a jetty nearby, until 1960 when road access was improved.

In 1864 the Monach Isles, 4 miles off North Uist, was another lighthouse built of brick. It would suffer a tragic accident on 15th November 1936. Principal Keeper J W Milne and his Assistant W Black had taken a dinghy over to the neighbouring island of Ceann Iar for supplies and mail but, returning in a blizzard, they were swept to their deaths by strong currents and winds. Milne's sister was able to report her predicament by radio and maintained the beacon herself overnight until help came next day. The bodies were washed ashore on the islands three weeks later. The Monach light was finally discontinued in 1942, during wartime, the last island family departing only months afterwards. Shillay is still owned by the NLB, and the whole island group is a National Nature Reserve.

Dubh Artach – the best architecturally

Two more lights were built in the Northern Isles in 1858 (Cantick Head, Orkney and Bressay, Shetland) but another challenge had long been lurking in the shadows – the vicious Torran Rocks 11 miles south of Mull. Nine miles beyond, they terminated in a lethal outcrop of Dubh Heartach - or Dubh Artach as it is now known. The urgency of the task was highlighted after severe storms in the vicinity during the winter of 1865, resulted in 24 vessels foundering in little more than a month. The rock is pounded with waves built up to spectacular proportions at Dubh Artach, across 2000 miles of open Atlantic. David and Thomas Stevenson realised that a tower of utmost strength was required on this rock only 10 metres above sea level. They estimated it would cost £56,900 and were given the authority to proceed in spring 1867 but it would be a further five years before the light was finally exhibited.

In 1890, in order to distinguish Dubh Artach's tower from its neighbour Skerryvore, 21 miles to the north, a red stripe was added to the former's white, wave-washed livery. Not surprisingly, given the difficulty of access and its unpopularity as a posting, Dubh Artach was one of the first rock lights to be automated in 1971. For some time the families of both Skerryvore and Dubh Artach keepers were domiciled at Earraid until finally transferring into Oban.

In 1872 David A Stevenson, David's son and Thomas's nephew, was to deem the sturdy, elegant tower as:

'One of the best architecturally in the service suiting as it does so well the rock on which it stands.'

Old painting of Dubh Artach under construction (NLB)

Strained relations

David and Thomas had already started another, but submerged, rock tower, further south, off the Isle of Man – **Chicken Rock**. By now both were also advising on projects in Japan, India, Newfoundland and New Zealand, as well as building harbours and breakwaters in Berwick, Eyemouth, Peterhead and Wick. Together, the brothers completed some 28 major lighthouses between 1854 and 1880.

Despite the demands of other engineering works, they both led full social lives at home in Edinburgh –giving lectures, writing scientific papers and reports, supporting local societies, their church and of course their families. Not surprisingly, with this arduous workload both David and Thomas began to suffer health problems. In 1881 David became so ill that he could no longer work and finally retired in 1883, leaving Tom to take over. After a long and illustrious career, as a most effective manager for the family firm, David died in 1885. He had been a man of sound judgement, upright, kind, open and approachable with wide interests - in railways, sewerage systems, agricultural implements and collecting artworks, while he had also travelled widely abroad. He had four daughters and four sons, but only two sons survived –both to become lighthouse engineers. When David died in 1886 the NLB were operating no fewer than 68 manned lighthouses. Alan Brebner had been made a full partner alongside David's two sons, David A and Charles, who assumed effective roles in the family firm - though Thomas always retained for himself the controlling shares. It remained a perennial source of bitterness for Tom that his own son, RLS, had proved totally disinterested in engineering.

Thomas was mortified when his nephew David Alan (David A.) was appointed as joint NLB engineer alongside him and relationships became very strained. Together they would be responsible for only three lights - Fidra in the Firth of Forth, Oxcars (a two-man light built in 1886 on the south shore of the Firth of Forth) and Ailsa Craig or 'Paddy's Milestone' off the Ayrshire coast.

As his health deteriorated Thomas became somewhat irrational and died in 1887. Perhaps, in atonement for failing follow in his father's footsteps, in 1886 Robert Louis Stevenson was moved to write of him:

'. . . he, two of my uncles, my grandfather, and my great grandfather in succession have been engineers to the Scotch Lighthouse Service; all the sea lights of Scotland are signed with our name, and my father's services to lighthouse optics have been distinguished indeed. I might write books till 1900 and not serve humanity so well; and it moves me to a certain impatience, to see the little, frothy bubble that attends the author his son, and compare it with the obscurity in which that better man finds his reward.'

' . . . The Bell Rock stands monument for my grandfather, the Skerry Vhor for my Uncle Alan; and when the lights come out at sundown along the shores of Scotland, I am proud to think they burn more brightly for the genius of my father.'

David A and Charles Stevenson

David Stevenson's two surviving sons, David Alan (1854 – 1938) and Charles Alexander (1855 – 1950) were to inherit the business. They were just as different as their father and uncle had been. Both had been groomed by their father, well educated to university level, travelled widely and enjoyed wide and varied interests, professionally and in their private lives. From the age of 17, under the guidance of his father and of Alan Brebner, David A. had developed a healthy passion for engineering. At 20 he had spent a summer at Erraid as Dubh Artach was being built and gained a commendation from the Institute of Civil Engineers for delivering a paper on the progress. At the same time, he followed his father's business interests in insurance, and had been elected a Fellow of the Royal Society of Edinburgh. Both boys shared their father's interest in archery, while Charles also enjoyed skating, horse riding, shooting, cycling and golf.

Charles was only a year younger but was impetuous and much less organised. He had an alert and inventive mind, with an intuitive approach to engineering. In America with his brother in 1877 he had seen a compressed air foghorn in operation and immediately saw its application for the NLB. A short time later he managed to have two sent to Scotland – which he installed at St Abbs and on Sanda. He had seen Alexander Graham Bell's telephone and its potential to provide communication from lightkeepers on remote stations such as Muckle Flugga and Skerryvore. He pondered how it could be altered to operate without wires and it is said that he came up with a system a year or two in advance of Marconi.

David A. would immediately step into his uncle's shoes as NLB Engineer, a post he was to retain tenaciously until his final retirement in 1938. However, David A. would only have daughters, and maybe felt the same element of resentment that his uncle Thomas had shown about handing over the reins to his nephew. Charles, meanwhile, still applied himself to civil work, and was happy to help iron out NLB problems for his brother who had to concentrate upon lighthouses, the associated paperwork and report writing. Together, just like the father and uncle, David A. and Charles complemented each other into a very effective team.

Financial restraints in the 1880s made the Board of Trade reluctant to take on new lights, so none showed in Scotland between 1886 and 1892. However, congestion and collisions in the English Channel were encouraging more and more ships to take a north-about route to and from the North Sea. Ships came to favour the Sumburgh passage nearer Shetland, rather than face the Pentland Firth. Between Orkney and Muckle Flugga there was only Sumburgh Head and it was obvious that more and better navigation lights were required. Thus the first crop of lighthouses the brothers David A. and Charles would tackle was in the north of Scotland, some of them as challenging as anything gone before.

Fair Isle, lying midway between Orkney and Shetland, was a good starting point, with lights to be exhibited at both its northern and southern extremities. David A. cut the first turf for the South Light in 1890 and the 26m tower was lit on 7th January 1892. The North Lighthouse (14 m high on a 75m cliff) came into service on 1st November that same year. Here the Stevensons had installed their first innovative 'hyper radiant' light, devised by Thomas and improved by Charles. The North Light became a rock station in 1978, when the families moved to Stromness, and it was eventually automated in 1981. With only 60 or so inhabitants the six lighthouse keepers and their families had contributed much to the little island community, especially numbers at the local school. In 1998 Fair Isle South became the last Scottish lighthouse to be automated, as described on its white-washed wall:

'Fair Isle South, the Last Manned Lighthouse in Scotland. This plaque commemorates the invaluable services of generations of lightkeepers from 1786 to 1998. Unveiled by HRH Princess Royal , Patron of the Northern Lighthouse Board. 31st March 1998'

Alongside this plaque, another commemorates tragedy. Fair Isle had suffered terribly during the Second World War – both lighthouses were hit by gunfire and bombs. In December 1941, Mrs Catherine Sutherland (aged 22), the wife of an assistant keeper, was killed and her infant daughter slightly hurt when a German bomber fired at the South Light. A few weeks later on 21st January 1942 the Luftwaffe returned and a bomb hit the main block. The wife of the Principal keeper, Mrs Margaret Smith (aged 50) and her 10 year old daughter Greta were killed. A soldier, William Morris, manning the nearby anti-aircraft gun nearby was also killed. In a remarkable devotion to duty, the assistant keeper at Fair Isle North, Roderick MacAulay, daily walked three miles through snow and gale force winds to help restore the South Light; he was awarded the BEM.

Fair Isle South lighthouse, Sheep Rock and crofts (J Love)

The Flannans – a mysterious disappearance

The brothers' major challenge however, would be the construction of the lighthouse on the Flannan Isles , a group of seven islands – sometimes referred to as 'The Seven Hunters' – lying some 20 miles west of the Isle of Lewis in the Outer Hebrides. But by now David A. was seriously ill with a nervous complaint. During long periods of convalescence Charles covered for him within the NLB, alongside pursuing his own inventions and engineering projects both at home and abroad. Notwithstanding, Charles liaised closely with his invalid brother to take on this new task.

The largest island Eilean Mor is only 29 acres so it was decided that the lighthouse would be a 'rock station' with a shore base for the families at Breasaclete in Lewis. David A. drew up his plans and a site chosen was on the grassy summit of the island 90 metres above sea level. Landings, even in calm weather were difficult as the island is surrounded by near perpendicular 50m cliffs. Two landing options were constructed, and two giant flights of steps had to be hewn out of the rock. All equipment then had to be got up to the site so a horse was slung ashore by crane to haul everything along a tramway to the summit. The points where the rails from east and west landings merged into one became known as 'Charing Cross'. (Sadly when Billy the horse came to be taken off, he struggled out of his sling and fell to his death into the sea below).

The site for the shore station at Breascelete was chosen for its close proximity to Loch Roag, a sea loch which provided a safe anchorage and shelter for the lighthouse tender. The lighthouse with its 23m tower took four years to construct. The light was exhibited on the 7th December 1899 when the engineers and workmen departed, leaving three keepers to maintain it. Four days later a crane at one of the landing stages was washed away in a furious gale but, as the weather allowed, fortnightly reliefs from Loch Roag were maintained - until an unparalleled disaster struck which brought the Flannan Isles lighthouse to the attention of the world.

December 1900, only a year after the light coming into service, proved particularly stormy and on the 15th a passing steamer failed to see any light flashing. Although *Hesperus* had been due to relieve the keepers on the 20th, bad weather meant it could not actually sail until Boxing Day. At noon it arrived at the Flannans when it was immediately obvious to the captain, crew and relief keeper Joseph Moore that all was not well. Moore's account of what he found, together with the Captain Harvie's report, are available on the NLB website.

Flannan Isles Lighthouse and old chapel (J Love)

All but the kitchen door was closed and the fire had not been made for several days. Inside the clock had stopped and the beds unmade. But everything else was in order, the lamps had been cleaned and refilled, while the blinds had been drawn around the lantern. It is usually said that there was an uneaten meal on the table, with an overtoppled chair beside it but Moore clearly states that:

'The kitchen utensils were all very clean, which is a sign that it must be after dinner sometime they left.'

There is no mention of any chair. Captain Harvie left Moore and three crew to tend the light, while he returned to Breasaclete on Loch Roag to notify NLB Head Office in Edinburgh. His telegram read:

'A dreadful accident has happened at Flannans. The three keepers, Ducat, Marshall and the Occasional have disappeared from the Island. On our arrival there this afternoon there was no signs of life to be seen . . . signs indicated that the accident must have happened about a week ago. Poor fellows they must have been blown over the cliffs or drowned trying to secure a crane or something like that. ..'

At the east landing everything was as it had been left on 7th December, the last relief. At the west landing however, there was chaos, dramatic evidence of the severity of the recent storms. Railings were bent, boxes and ropes strewn around and a block of stone weighing more than a ton had moved position. Two hundred feet above the sea turf had been ripped off the cliff top.

The log book had been kept up until Saturday the 15th December. It must be assumed that the men disappeared that afternoon. The official conclusion was that the three keepers had gone down to the landing in the storm to secure the gear but were washed away in a great wave. No bodies were ever found. The men left two widows and six children.

All sorts of fanciful stories have arisen as to what might have happened, most of them ludicrous. But there seems no reason to doubt Captain Harvie's initial assessment – the men had got washed away in the storm. It was only in 1912 when an English poet Wilfrid William Gibson (1878-1962) published his epic Flannan Isle that the story began to assume an air of mystique:

> *'Though three men dwelt on Flannan Isle*
> *To keep the lamp alight*
> *As we steered under the lee, we caught*
> *No glimmer through the night . . .*
>
> *. . . Of the three men's fate we found no trace*
> *Of any kind in any place,*
> *But a door ajar and an untouched meal*
> *And an overtoppled chair . . .*
>
> *. . . We seemed to stand for an endless while*
> *Though still no word was said .*
> *Three men alive on Flannan Isle,*
> *Who thought on three men dead.'*

Thus arose the myth of the untouched meal and an overtoppled chair; poetic devices to add melodrama reminiscent of the *Marie Celeste*. Gibson even went on to mention '*how the rock had been the death of many a likely lad*' but the light had only been lit for a year! Since Gibson, there have been written various songs, at least one novel, an opera by Sir Peter Maxwell Davis and even a video game. And thus the mystery endures. . .

The station became automatic in September 1971 and the keepers withdrawn. The light was converted from acetylene gas to solar power in 1999 and, like all other NLB lights now, is monitored from Headquarters in 84 George Street, Edinburgh.

The west landing, Flannan Isles (J Love)

A new century

At the start of the twentieth century the Commissioners were keen to fill some of the 'dark blanks' remaining on the Scottish coast. One of the first was Tiumpan Head on Lewis, overlooking the Minch, the light being exhibited on 1 December 1900. The station was automated in 1985.

By the start of the 20th century there had been several fatal wrecks in the Firth of Forth so in addition to Fidra, lighthouses were deemed necessary at Barns Ness and Bass Rock. In 1904 another Heisgeir, often incorrectly referred to as Oigh Sgeir, was completed on a low-lying 10-acre skerry of columnar basalt, 6 miles west of Canna in the Inner Hebrides. With their families living in Oban, the duty keepers on Heisgeir kept a walled garden on this sea-washed rock, which grew wonderful beetroot, cabbages, onions etc. said to be the most productive garden the keepers had ever seen. They also kept three goats for fresh milk but by 1980 when I visited the rock, only one called Maisie was left. The keepers also created a three-hole golf course! In 1938 Heisgeir rock was bought by John Lorne Campbell of Canna, a Gaelic scholar and keen lepidopterist, who encouraged the keepers to collect moths for him – surely the largest moth trap in the world! The light was automated in 1997.

Heisgeir lighthouse and landing stage 1980 (J Love)

In 1904, when aged 13, Charles's son David Alan (D.Alan) was taken on his first inspection voyage and began learning the ropes in the office. He was a strong boy graduating B.Sc. at Edinburgh by 1912. His uncle now had some 90 lighthouses under his charge (compared with 30 when Skerryvore came on stream). Maughold Head on the Isle of Man was in progress and many lights were undergoing refurbishment, incorporating Charles's more modern lamps.

At this time the NLB found it difficult to experiment with new ideas without seeking sanction from Trinity House and the Board of Trade, so the Stevensons usually circumvented these issues by using the independent Clyde Lighthouse Trust. Charles installed acetylene gas power at Cloch lighthouse in 1900, with such success that Cumbrae was also fitted in 1908. With his son he also developed the 'Leader Cable' for guiding ships through narrow channels; an electric cable laid on the seabed was detected on board the ship to keep it on track.

Other lighthouses coming into service before the First World War were Noup Head on the Orkney island of Westray in1908, Holy Island (1905), Neist Point in Skye (1909) and Rudh' Reidh on the coast of Wester Ross (1912). Neist Point lighthouse looked across the Minch to Ushenish in South Uist which David Stevenson had built half a century earlier. Ushenish was automated in 1970 and monitored by the keepers in Neist Point 18 miles away, until it too went automatic in 1990.

Neist Point, Isle of Skye (J Love)

The Great War and after

War was nothing new to the lighthouse service, but the 20th century conflicts were in a different league. Many lighthouses were strafed by enemy aircraft and, tragically, Fair Isle South incurred several casualties. All but the most vital lights were extinguished all round the British coast so that enemy mine-layers could no longer orientate. Keepers would be sent signals if Royal Navy movements were anticipated. In October 1915 the Bell Rock never received the warning and, with no guiding light, the troopship HMS *Argyll* foundered on the reef. The three keepers managed to get a line aboard and the full complement of 650 men were rescued. In fact one keeper got his foot tangled in a rope and nearly became the sole casualty. Six weeks later the Admiralty installed telegraphic communications between Bell Rock and Fife Ness.

The NLB were being pressured to provide for great naval bases such as Rosyth, Cromarty and Scapa Flow. Copinsay in Orkney was built in 1915 because of the increased naval activity around Scapa Flow, although it was not lit officially until after the hostilities in 1919.

Copinsay lighthouse, Orkney (J Love)

By now Charles Stevenson was over 70 yet, in 1929, he and his son D. Alan collaborated on their greatest invention to date – the 'Talking Beacon'. A radio signal from a ship received cross-bearings from two shore stations which then allowed it to calculate its position. The Stevensons had improved on earlier American / RAF prototypes by compensating for the time lag and any distortion from surrounding hills. Despite his stammer D. Alan introduced the invention at an international conference in 1929 when, at the same time, a prototype was installed at Cumbrae. It became an overnight sensation and was quickly adopted worldwide. Sadly however Britain was slow to take up the idea and Cumbrae remained the only Talking Beacon, until overtaken by radar some ten years later.

After the war the NLB resumed work, with lighthouses being built at Duncansby (1924) and Esha Ness in Shetland (1929). Tor Ness in Orkney (1937) became the last major Stevenson lighthouse. The family firm was renamed C & A Stevenson, leaving an ageing and ailing David A. to his NLB Engineer's post and with no son to assume his mantle. The situation that had prevailed between his own father and uncle was recreated. His nephew D. Alan became increasingly frustrated and impatient with the NLB. He was always rather blunt and outspoken so when David A. finally retired in 1938, the NLB passed by D. Alan and appointed another assistant, John Oswald, in his stead. David A. died only a month later.

In 1940 Charles retired and, after wartime service erecting lighthouses in the Dardanelles, D. Alan became engaged in further Admiralty work on the Clyde before finally retiring himself in 1952. He had now become the family historian, publishing a book in 1949 on Robert Stevenson's *English Lighthouse Tours*, and then another on *The World's Lighthouses* before 1820 ten years later; but his magnum opus on the Stevenson dynasty was never to be finished. Late in 1971, aged 80, he was admitted to hospital and died three weeks later.

Craig Mair reflected on the Stevenson legacy:

'Their integrity was unfailing. Their busy lives were unpretentious. Their work was creative and important, for even today how many unknown sailors owe them their lives? And yet there is one last, still more revealing, facet of their work. Although they were responsible for so many brilliant inventions, not a single Stevenson ever seems to have taken out a patent. They could have been millionaires but they chose to give their gifts to the world. It was an extraordinary gesture, but then, they were remarkable people.'

In 1958 the last manned lighthouse in Scotland was built at Strathy Point, Caithness on the north coast of Scotland by the NLB Engineer Peter Hyslop.

Rockall

On June 1972 the Government despatched 'a combined expedition' to 'set up a flashing navigational beacon' on Rockall as an aid to shipping. There was little doubt that the motive was just as much political. Rockall, only 30 metres across and 24m in height, lay 250 miles west of the Outer Hebrides. But with a prospect of oil discoveries in its waters, it assumed an importance greatly in excess of its size. A government report concluded:

'There can be no place more desolate, despairing and awful . . . More people have landed on the moon than have landed on Rockall.'

That may no longer be true but the reliability of the beacon, and its successors, falls far short of any navigational function, especially in winter storms but it can claim to be the most isolated lighthouse in the world!

Oil developments

In 1978 when oil tankers began using Sullom Voe, the largest oil terminal in Britain, a couple of new lights were needed in Shetland. An 'outside route' beyond the Hebrides, also necessitated the construction of further automatic lighthouses on North Rona (commissioned in 1984) with a beacon on Sulaisgeir 11 miles away (also 1984), both of which were to be monitored by UHF link by the keepers at the Butt of Lewis. It was this monitoring requirement that determined which stations were the last to be manned – Fair Isle South, Rinns of Islay, Cape Wrath, Kinnaird Head and St Abbs Head. But the sophistication of computer technology quickly rendered this arrangement redundant and operations could be directed from a single Monitor Centre in Edinburgh, which soon afterwards took control of all buoys and lighthouses, over 350 of them.

Erecting the new lighthouse on Hasker, Outer Hebrides (J Love)

After the fully-laden tanker *Braer* went aground in January 1993, the Donaldson Report recommended four further lights be commissioned – one near Kyle of Lochalsh, and three west of the Outer Hebrides. The major light on Haskeir deployed a hybrid solar/wind powered renewable energy source - the first of its kind. Minor lights were erected on Gasker just to the north and on the Monach Isles beside the old brick tower abandoned during the Second War. All three were completed in 200 days between April and October 1997, when I was able to visit them by helicopter with the NLB Engineer. Then after a review in 2005, it was decided to increase the range on Monach from 10 miles to 18 miles, for which the most attractive option was to move back into the old tower. The NLB proudly reported :

'As a result of the combination of exposed off-shore location, natural heritage value (seals and seabirds), cultural heritage value (Grade B Listed Buildings), contemporary health and safety demands and financial constraints, the project to re-light the Monach Isles lighthouse provides an excellent example of the type of work we do in the Projects Section of the Engineers Department. . . It is heartening to see that, despite the passage of almost 150 years and advances in navigation technology, the original Stevenson-designed Monach Isles lighthouse still has a vital role in the provision of a major aid to navigation.'

Heisgeir brick light tower recommissioned in 2005 (J Love)

Many other lighthouses are now being converted to mains electricity or solar electric power, with backup diesel and wind generation. Despite devolution the NLB remains under the remit of the Department of Transport in London but, where there had been some friction in the past, the NLB and Trinity House co-operate closely, and with the Commissioners of Irish Lights. All three are active members of the International Association of Marine Aids to Navigation and Lighthouse Authorities (IALA). Thus while the very last Scottish foghorn was turned off at Skerryvore in 2005, the lights continue shining.

An ocean-going ship's master commented:

'I have all the modern navigational equipment on board, but there is nothing more friendly and welcoming than the sight of a flashing lighthouse.'

Looking out to Heisgeir, off Canna. (J Love)

As for the Stevensons, the 'black sheep' of the family and famous author Robert Louis can have the last word:

' In the afternoon of time
a strenuous family dusted from its hands
the sands of granite and, beholding far
along the sounding coasts its pyramids
and tall memorials catch the dying sun,
smiled well content. . .'

Puffins on Sule Skerry, Orkney (J Love)

The quarters at Breasaclete, Lewis for the families of the Flannan Isles lightkeepers (J Love)

Further Reading

Allardyce, Keith and Evelyn M Hood (1986) *At Scotland's Edge*. Collins, London.

Bathurst, Bella (1999) *The Lighthouse Stevensons*. Harper Collins, London.

Krauskopf, Sharma (2001) *Scottish Lighthouses*. Appletree Press, Belfast.

Leslie, Jean and Roland Paxton (1999) *Bright Lights: the Stevenson Engineers 1752-1971*. Privately published by the authors, Edinburgh

Mair, Craig (1978) *A Star for Seamen: the Stevenson Family of Engineers*. John Murray, London.

Morrison-Low, A D (2010) *Northern Lights; the age of Scottish Lighthouses*. National Museums of Scotland.

Munro, R W (1979) *Scottish Lighthouses*. Thule Press, Stornoway.

Nicholson, Christopher (2006) *Rock Lighthouses of Britain*. Whittles Publishing.

Paxton, Roland (2011) *Dynasty of Engineers: The Stevensons and the Bell Rock*. Northern Lighthouse Heritage Trust, Edinburgh.